Advent
IS FOR WAITING

By Donna R. Rathert

Illustrated by Gordon Willman

Copyright © 1986 Concordia Publishing House
3558 S. Jefferson Avenue, St. Louis, MO 63118-3968
Manufactured in the United States of America

Library of Congress Cataloging-in-Publication Data

Rathert, Donna, 1949-
    Advent is for waiting.

    Summary: Explains the religious decorations, symbols, terms, and activities encountered during Advent, the preparation to celebrate the birth of Jesus. Suggests related activities for parent and child.
    1. Advent—Juvenile literature. [1. Advent] I. Willman, Gordon, ill. II. Title.
BV40.R37 1986   263'.91   85-27003
ISBN 0-570-04140-6

2   3   4   5   6   7   8   9   10   PP   95   94   93   92   91   90   89   88

For Adrienne,
My Advent Angel

It's December—
time for

ADVENT.

Advent is a waiting time.
It's the time we wait for Christmas.
Christmas is Jesus' birthday!

Here's an ADVENT WREATH.

It helps us wait for Jesus' birthday.
See how the green branches make a circle?
The circle reminds us that God's love
    never ends.

This Advent wreath is in a church.
Look at the pretty purple candles!

There's one for each Sunday in Advent.
See? I can count them!
When they're all lit, Christmas is
   very close.

Look!
There's also an Advent
   in my church.
The banner tells me that
Jesus' birthday is coming soon.

And, Pastor's wearing
an Advent

STOLE

to match the color
of the altar covers.
The color means,
"Jesus is King!"

Some churches have special Advent services.
Listen! I hear some special Advent words:

Watch! Now the

MANGER SCENE
is going up!

See? There's Mary and Joseph.
But, wait! Where's Baby Jesus?
That's right!
They put Him   in the manger on Christmas Eve.

Hey! Do you see?
Our church's Christmas tree is up.
It has many

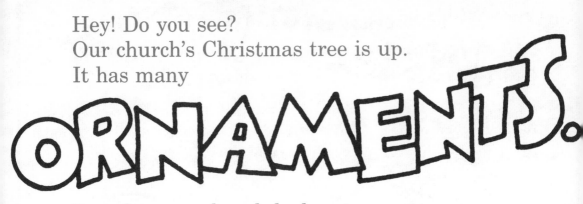

ORNAMENTS.

It makes our church look extra pretty.

Now, I wonder . . . .
What can *I* do
to get ready for

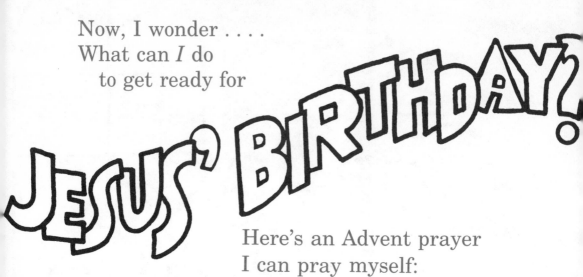

JESUS' BIRTHDAY?

Here's an Advent prayer
I can pray myself:

Come, Lord Jesus,
Be my Friend.
I'm glad Your love
   will never end.
Amen.

It's hard to wait for Christmas
But, that's what

is all about.
Advent is a waiting time!
We're waiting to celebrate Jesus' birthday.

A NOTE TO PARENTS

The commercial Christmas comes earlier and earlier each year. As Christians we have the opportunity to put off the Christmas rush. We celebrate Advent—a gentle waiting time, a proper preparation for a hearty appreciation of Jesus' birthday.

Advent Is for Waiting can help you enrich this waiting time for your children.

Here are some ways to use this book:

1. Let your child color in the book during worship services. To extend it's use, laminate the pages with clear contact paper, which wipes clean for reuse.

2. Read the book at home with your child several times during Advent.

3. Point out to your child your church's particular Advent rituals and customs and explain them. Personalize the goings-on so that your child feels free to participate with joy.

4. Celebrate Advent at home. Make an Advent wreath and use it as a focus for (or addition to) your family prayer time. Get an Advent calendar and make a ritual of its daily use.

5. Help your children enter into the reality of the Christmas story. Let them have their own manger scene with moveable figures to act out the holy drama. Talk with your child about the specialness of the story for Christians. Remind your children this really happened. Jesus really was born—just as we were.

6. Watch your own Advent attitude. How does your child view *you* these days? By your example, show your own personal preparation for Jesus' birthday.

"Prepare the way for the Lord," says Matt. 3:3 (NIV). May you do so with vigor!

A blessed Advent to you,
     Donna R. Rathert